T3-BWO-394

Glossary

Subhanallah - Glory to Allah

Alhamdulillah - All praise is for Allah

Inshallah - Allah willing

Bismillah - In the Name of Allah

Mashallah - It is as Allah has pleased

KIDS will be **KIDS**

Published by Kids Will Be Kids
Copyright © 2007 By Nabeel Akbar. All rights reserved.

Distributed by Kube Publishing Ltd.
MCC, Ratby Lane, Markfield, Leicestershire, LE67 9SY, UK
Tel: +44 (0)1530 249230 Fax: +44 (0)1530 249656
E-mail: info@kubepublishing.com Website: www.kubepublishing.com

ISBN 978-0-980938-21-0
Hardback Edition Designed by: Nasir Cadir
Coordinator: Anwar Cara

Visit us at www.kidswillbekids.org

Bedtime Shorts:

To Catch a bug

Written by Nabeel Akbar

Illustrated by Anam Ahmed

There's always a lot to discover outside in the fresh air.
I love to just sit in the backyard garden and stare.

It's not the pretty flowers that catch my eye.
I'm looking for spiders, bugs and maybe a butterfly.

I love to watch them as they crawl around,
Subhanallah, they move without making a sound.

Some are very colourful and bright,
Alhamdulillah, it's a beautiful sight.

Others are dark with more legs than can be counted.
Morphing into a different shape, they'll leave you astounded.

Inshallah, I think I'll try and catch one today.
Then I'll show mom, I wonder what she'll say.

Of course I'll be careful
when catching the insect.
It's important to show all
of Allah's creatures respect.

I grab some empty jars, and in the lids I poke a few holes.
Bismillah, I catch the first bug and into the jar it rolls.

Next I catch a spider,
then a cute lady bug,
Then comes a caterpillar,
followed by a slimy slug.

I take all the jars inside to keep,
I'll catch a few more and my collection will be complete!

Suddenly, from inside my house comes a loud shriek!
I quickly run in to take a peek.

I see my mother with a look
of fear in her eyes.
'Mommy!' I shout, 'I caught
these bugs for you as a surprise!'

"Mashallah," she says, "that was very sweet of you dear,"
"But when it comes to bugs, mommy has a little fear,"

'So I'd appreciate if you keep the bugs outside when you play.'
'No problem mommy!' I reply, 'I'll do exactly as you say.'

So I'm not allowed to bring anymore bugs into the house. But mom didn't say anything about bringing in...